TABLE OF CONTENTS

Can you drive a car or ride a bicycle? If so, you can probably pilot an airplane!

Find us on Facebook for training tips, aviation news, and product information.
www.facebook.com/gleimaviation

LEARNING TO FLY: IT'S EASY!

It's fun to learn to fly and earn a pilot certificate. The thrill of flying is achieved through personal accomplishments and comes with unparalleled excitement and freedom. You may want to become a sport or private pilot for the privilege of flying yourself to thousands of airports. If your goal is to become a commercial or airline pilot, the opportunities you will discover also bring an alluring responsibility. Flying can change how you approach many facets of life.

A New Experience

Most people believe airplanes are to be ridden in as a passenger, rather than flown as a pilot. In contrast, when you see a nice automobile, you project yourself into the driver's seat and imagine yourself driving. The next time you see an airplane, imagine yourself flying it as the pilot. You're sitting in the left seat, feeling in control and ready to take to the skies.

Flying an airplane is more complex than driving a car. In addition to controlling the left-right movements of the airplane, you are controlling altitude (up and down). These complexities make flying more exhilarating than driving because you have the freedom of three-dimensional movement, greater speed, and spectacular panoramas. Flying provides lifelong satisfaction and pride.

Earning Your Pilot Certificate

Many people might consider learning to fly beyond their capability or budget, but it is not as difficult, time consuming, or expensive as is generally believed.

The Federal Aviation Administration (FAA) regulates pilot privileges and issues pilot certificates. Earning a pilot certificate requires specific flight experience, a knowledge test, and a practical (flight) test. Use Gleim Aviation to learn more about pilot training. This "Learn to Fly–Become a Pilot" booklet provides ideal advance preparation for introductory flights and traditional pilot training.

The next time you see an airplane, imagine yourself flying it as the pilot.

GET PAID TO FLY DRONES!

In the past few years, the aviation industry has seen a significant shift toward the use of Unmanned Aerial Systems (UAS). The highly-anticipated Part 107 small Unmanned Aerial Systems (sUAS or "drones") rule was announced in 2016, finalizing the first operational rules for commercial sUAS operations. According to industry estimates, the rule could generate more than $82 billion for the U.S. economy and create more than 100,000 new jobs over 10 years.

Why Regulate Drone Operations?

The Part 107 rule streamlined the process to operate sUAS for hire by removing cumbersome requirements for routine commercial operations, which were previously met through a lengthy FAA approval process.

This is a new era in aviation and the potential for unmanned aircraft will make it far safer and easier to do certain jobs, gather information, and deploy disaster relief. To minimize risks, training is required for the thousands of operators expected to become a Remote Pilot in Command.

Becoming a Remote Pilot

A new type of pilot's license, called the Remote Pilot Certificate, is required to fly drones for commercial purposes. The training to earn this certificate can be completed quickly and affordably. Remote pilots must learn about a wide range of topics to safely integrate their operations into the National Airspace System.

sUAS operators have opportunities in nearly every industry. Gleim Aviation is excited to help usher in this new era of aviation with training that ensures safety and responsible flying is a top priority for all operators. To learn more about remote pilot training and opportunities, refer to Part 6, "Remote Pilot Training," beginning on page 41, or visit our drones information page online at www.GleimAviation.com/drones.

This is a new era in aviation and the potential for unmanned aircraft will make it far safer and easier to do certain jobs, gather information, and deploy disaster relief.

TO: **Pilots and Potential Pilots**

FROM: **Irvin N. Gleim, Ph.D., CFII**

We prepare valuable, user-friendly self-study materials that are highly effective. Just as a carefully prepared teacher can present a class that helps you learn, our carefully designed books, FAA Test Prep Online, Audio Review, and online courses will make it easy for you to learn and understand.

*We convert the FAA test process from a memorization marathon into a learning opportunity and rewarding experience. You will get higher test scores in less study time. Our products are **NOT** additional work; they are designed to save you time, effort, frustration, and money.*

1.1 SEVEN BASIC STEPS TO YOUR SPORT OR PRIVATE PILOT CERTIFICATE

1. Purchase the Gleim **Deluxe Sport Pilot** or **Private Pilot Kit with Online Ground School**.
2. Prepare for and pass the FAA Pilot Knowledge Test.
3. Obtain a student pilot certificate.
4. For private pilot, obtain at least a third-class medical certificate from an FAA-approved doctor. For sport pilot, your driver's license substitutes for a medical certificate.
5. Select a flight instructor and/or flight school.
6. Complete your flight training by utilizing Gleim *Pilot Syllabus* and *Flight Maneuvers* books (included in Gleim pilot kits).
7. Pass an FAA flight test called the practical test.

1.2 THREE BASIC STEPS TO YOUR REMOTE PILOT CERTIFICATE

1. Learn the aeronautical knowledge subjects applicable to drone operators using Gleim remote pilot training resources.
2. Pass the FAA Unmanned Aircraft–General exam.
3. Apply online for your Remote Pilot Certificate with the FAA.

1.3 WHAT IS A STUDENT PILOT CERTIFICATE?

Getting a student pilot certificate is one of the first steps toward earning a sport pilot or private pilot certificate. This certificate must be obtained before you are allowed to fly solo.

You must be at least 16 years of age and be able to read, speak, and understand English to receive a student pilot certificate. To apply, you will meet in person with a Flight Instructor, FAA inspector at a local Flight Standards District Office, designated pilot examiner, or airman certificate representative from an approved 14 CFR Part 141 flight school. An application will be processed and sent to the FAA and TSA for review. Upon approval, your student pilot certificate will be mailed.

1.4   WHAT IS A MEDICAL CERTIFICATE?

UNITED STATES OF AMERICA

UNITED STATES OF AMERICA
Department of Transportation   **BB**-5342031
Federal Aviation Administration
MEDICAL CERTIFICATE ___3rd___ **CLASS**

This certifies that *(Full name and address)*:

Graves, John Mortimer
1234 W. 56 St.
Gainesville, FL 32605

Date of Birth	Ht.	Wt.	Hair	Eyes	Sex
1/23/86	5'9"	150	Brn.	Brn.	M

has met the medical standards prescribed in Part 67 Federal Aviation Regulations for this class of Medical Certificate, and the standards prescribed on Part 61 for a Student Pilot Certificate.

Limitations

None

Date of Examination	Examiner's Serial No.
4/15/17	12345-6

Examiner

Signature   *J. T. Taylor, D.O.*
Typed Name   J. T. Taylor, D.O.

AIRMAN'S SIGNATURE
John Mortimer Graves

FAA Form 8420-2 (7-92) Supersedes Previous Edition

If you desire a private pilot certificate, you must obtain at least a third-class medical certificate. If you desire a sport pilot certificate, you may substitute a medical certificate with a valid U.S. driver's license. The FAA medical examination is a routine exam administered by FAA-designated doctors called aviation medical examiners (AMEs), who will issue your medical certificate after the exam.

Even if you have a physical handicap, medical certificates can be issued in many cases. Operating limitations may be imposed depending upon the nature of the disability.

Visit www.faa.gov/pilots/amelocator for a list of AMEs by state and city. Call (800) 874-5346 if you have questions.

1.5   WHAT IS A PRIVATE PILOT CERTIFICATE?

Obtaining a private pilot certificate allows you to fly an airplane and carry passengers and baggage. Although operating expenses may be equally shared with your passengers, you may not fly for "compensation or hire." The certificate is sent to you by the FAA upon satisfactory completion of your training program, a knowledge test, and a practical test. A sample private pilot certificate is reproduced to the right.

1.6   WHAT IS A SPORT PILOT CERTIFICATE?

The sport pilot certificate is available specifically for pilots of light-sport aircraft (LSA). An LSA is a small, simple-to-operate, low-performance airplane, glider, powered parachute, etc. The light-sport airplane is usually smaller and slower than other light airplanes. A sport pilot certificate and LSAs are a good way for sport pilots to fly at less cost. Sport pilots may carry one passenger.

1.7 FAA REQUIREMENTS TO OBTAIN A SPORT OR PRIVATE PILOT CERTIFICATE

1. Be at least 17 years of age [when you finish your training and take your FAA practical (flight) test].

2. Be able to read, speak, write, and understand English.

3. Obtain at least a third-class FAA medical certificate (or a driver's license for sport pilot).

4. Obtain a student pilot certificate.

5. Pass the pilot knowledge test with a score of 70% or better. All FAA tests are administered at FAA-designated computer testing centers.

    a. The sport pilot knowledge test consists of 40 multiple-choice questions.
    b. The private pilot knowledge test consists of 60 multiple-choice questions.
    c. Sample questions, answers, and complete answer explanations are provided in the Gleim *FAA Knowledge Test Prep* book, **FAA Test Prep Online**, and **Online Ground School**.

6. Undertake flight training as described in the Gleim *Sport Pilot Syllabus* or *Private Pilot Syllabus* for the sport or private certificate, respectively. Many of the lessons will require more than one flight to make you comfortable and proficient.

    a. For a sport pilot certificate, you must receive a minimum of 20 hours of flight training, including a minimum of 5 hours of solo (i.e., by yourself) flight time.
    b. For a private pilot certificate issued under Part 61 of the Federal Aviation Regulations, you must receive a minimum of 40 hours of flight time, including a minimum of 10 hours of solo flight time in an airplane.
    c. As an alternative to Part 61 training, you may enroll in an FAA-certificated pilot school that has an approved private pilot certification course.

        1) These schools are known as Part 141 schools because they are authorized by Part 141 of the Federal Aviation Regulations.
        2) The Part 141 course must consist of at least 35 hours of ground training and 35 hours of flight training.
        3) There is little difference between Part 61 training and Part 141 training, except that a Part 61 course has more flexibility to adjust to your individual needs.

7. Successfully complete a practical (flight) test, which will be given as a final exam by an FAA evaluator, usually called a designated pilot examiner. Each of the required tasks/maneuvers for the sport and private flight tests is both explained and illustrated in the Gleim *Flight Maneuvers and Practical Test Prep* books for sport and private pilots.

    a. FAA-designated pilot examiners are proficient, experienced flight instructors/pilots who are authorized by the FAA to conduct practical tests. They typically charge a fee for their services.
    b. If you use the Gleim *Private Pilot Flight Maneuvers and Practical Test Prep* or *Sport Pilot Flight Maneuvers and Practical Test Prep* book, you will pass your FAA practical test with CONFIDENCE!

    If you have any questions now or throughout your flight training, call 800-874-5346 or contact us at www.GleimAviation.com/questions. We're here to help.
    Get started on your flight training by ordering your Gleim **Pilot Kit** today.

1.8 FLIGHT TRAINING

1. Visit several flight schools, if more than one is available, to talk to flight instructors about flight lessons. Visit www.GleimAviation.com/findacfi (our CFI Directory) to locate a CFI near you. Alternatively, look under aircraft schools, airplane instruction, aircraft sales, airports, etc., in the Yellow Pages or search online. Indicate that you are interested in taking flying lessons and want to choose a flight instructor with whom you will feel comfortable.

    Make sure the CFI is familiar with the Gleim pilot training materials (the books with the red covers) and is enthusiastic about using them. If you encounter hesitation, call Gleim at 800-874-5346.

    Plan to speak to several instructors. While there are no perfect answers, the following questions should be asked. The objective of these questions is to gain insight into the flight instructor's personality.

    a. Do you instruct full- or part-time? This information concerns availability only. Part-time does **not** imply less proficiency.
    b. May I review your syllabus? Compare it to your Gleim *Pilot Syllabus*.
    c. How long does your average student take to solo? Note that the flight instructor who solos his or her students in the least or most amount of time may not necessarily be the best instructor.
    d. How many total hours of solo and dual flight do your typical students require?
    e. For the private pilot certificate, what percentage of your students require more than 40 total hours? (Probably 100%.) How many more hours do they require? A national average of 55+ flight hours is often quoted.
    f. What are the solo and dual rental costs for your training aircraft?
    g. Where do you recommend that I take my pilot knowledge and practical tests, and what are the estimated costs?
    h. Where do you recommend that I take my medical examination?
    i. What is your (flight instructor's) schedule and the schedule of available aircraft?
    j. Do you have an introductory flight for a nominal fee? May I take it with no further obligation?

2. Once you have made a preliminary choice of flight instructor, you need to sit down with your flight instructor and map out a plan.

    a. When and how often you will fly
    b. When you will take the FAA pilot knowledge test
    c. When you should plan to take your FAA practical test
    d. When and how payments will be made for your instruction

3. Once you begin your pilot training, purchase a local sectional chart, a Chart Supplement, and a copy of your airplane's Pilot Operating Handbook (POH) or Airplane Flight Manual (AFM).

4. Consider purchasing an airplane (by yourself or through joint ownership) or joining a flying club. Sharing expenses through joint ownership can reduce the cost of flying. Insuring a plane, especially for a student, should not pose too much of an additional expense – especially if the airplane you insure is of the typical training variety (i.e., a simple, low-horsepower, single-engine airplane). However, it is always a good idea to contact an aviation insurance company/broker to discuss your insurance needs prior to the purchase of an airplane.

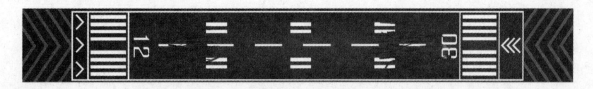

1.9   PART 61 VS. PART 141 TRAINING

Students often hear and ask about the difference between 14 CFR Part 61 and 14 CFR Part 141 flight training. Part 61 vs. Part 141 training refers to the section in the Federal Aviation Regulations defining minimum pilot training requirements and certification of flight schools.

Any Certificated Flight Instructor (CFI) or flight school can train pilots under Part 61. Flight schools can become FAA-approved under Part 141, which requires certain standards to be met under strict FAA regulations. Part 141 schools are directly overseen by the FAA and must meet minimum passing rates for pilot certification.

Part 141 schools typically have a more rigid structure, while Part 61 schools tend to have more flexibility. It is important to consider how you learn, what your goals are as a pilot, and your availability to attend lessons. These factors will help you decide which type of training and school is best for you.

Flight Training

Part 141 schools can allow a student to complete the training in fewer hours. For private pilot training, the minimum flight training requirements are reduced from 40 hours for training under Part 61, to 35 hours under Part 141. Considering that most students do not earn their certificates at the FAA minimums, this might not make much of a difference for your initial training. However, subsequent courses can be completed in significantly less time. For commercial pilot training, Part 141 students only need 190 hours of aeronautical experience, compared to 250 hours for Part 61 students.

Ground Training

Each course also requires ground school training. Part 141 students must have 35 hours of formal ground school training. Part 61 students do not need to receive a minimum amount of ground training; however, the same topics must still be learned. It is important to note that students who spend more time studying and learning during ground school typically finish their flight training faster.

Regardless of which type of school you attend, you will need to gain the same aeronautical knowledge and meet the same performance standards when you take your FAA knowledge test and practical exam.

If you are considering a career as a professional pilot, prefer a more rigid structure, and enjoy fast-paced training, then a Part 141 school might be the best option for you. If you enjoy more flexibility and prefer part-time training, then consider enrolling in a Part 61 school. If you are not sure, you should try to visit both types of schools. Tour the facilities, interview the staff and instructors, and discuss your aviation goals to see for yourself which one you prefer.

1.10 GLEIM ONLINE GROUND SCHOOL

1. The Gleim **Online Ground School** course content is based on the Gleim *FAA Knowledge Test Prep* books, **FAA Test Prep Online**, FAA publications, and Gleim reference books. Gleim even guarantees Online Ground School graduates will pass the FAA knowledge exam or we will refund the purchase price of your course.

    a. Online Ground School courses are available for

        1) Sport Pilot
        2) Private Pilot
        3) Instrument Pilot
        4) Commercial Pilot
        5) Fundamentals of Instructing
        6) Flight or Ground Instructor
        7) Airline Transport Pilot
        8) Flight Engineer
        9) Canadian Certificate Conversion
        10) Military Competency

    b. These courses are airplane-only and have the same study unit order as the Gleim *FAA Knowledge Test Prep* books.

    c. Each course contains study outlines that automatically reference current FAA publications, the appropriate knowledge test questions, and FAA figures. Gleim answer explanations are expertly written to explain the correct and incorrect answers.

    d. Online Ground School is always up to date.

    e. Users achieve very high knowledge test scores and a near-100% pass rate.

    f. **The Gleim Online Ground School is the most flexible course available!** Access your personal classroom from any computer with Internet access 24 hours a day, 7 days a week. Your virtual classroom is never closed!

Number	Study Unit	Status	Score	Time Started	Time Completed	A/V	Outline	Action
1	Airplanes and Aerodynamics	Not Started	N/A	N/A	N/A			Start
2	Airplane Instruments, Engines, and Systems	Not Started	N/A	N/A	N/A			Start
3	Airports, Air Traffic Control, and Airspace	Not Started	N/A	N/A	N/A			Start
4	Federal Aviation Regulations	Not Started	N/A	N/A	N/A			Start
5	Airplane Performance and Weight and Balance	Not Started	N/A	N/A	N/A			Start
	Stage Test #1	Not Started	N/A	N/A	N/A	N/A	N/A	
6	Aeromedical Factors and Aeronautical Decision Making (ADM)	Not Started	N/A	N/A	N/A			
7	Aviation Weather	Not Started	N/A	N/A	N/A			
8	Aviation Weather Services	Not Started	N/A	N/A	N/A			
9	Navigation: Charts and Publications	Not Started	N/A	N/A	N/A			
10	Navigation Systems	Not Started	N/A	N/A	N/A			
11	Cross-Country Flight Planning	Not Started	N/A	N/A	N/A			
	Stage Test #2	Not Started	N/A	N/A	N/A	N/A	N/A	
	End-Of-Course Test	Not Started	N/A	N/A	N/A	N/A	N/A	
	Practice Test #1	Not Started	N/A	N/A	N/A	N/A	N/A	
	Practice Test #2	Not Started	N/A	N/A	N/A	N/A	N/A	
	Practice Test #3	Not Started	N/A	N/A	N/A	N/A	N/A	
	Practice Test #4	Not Started	N/A	N/A	N/A	N/A	N/A	
	Practice Test #5	Not Started	N/A	N/A	N/A	N/A	N/A	

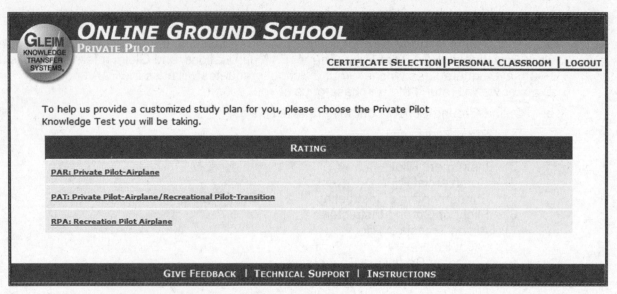

g. **Save time and study only the material you need to know!** The Gleim **Online Ground School** Certificate Selection will provide you with a guided study plan. You save time with integrated quizzes and practice exam simulations.

h. **Focus on your weak areas with our interactive course.** Explanations of incorrect answer choices help you learn from your mistakes, improving your knowledge faster.

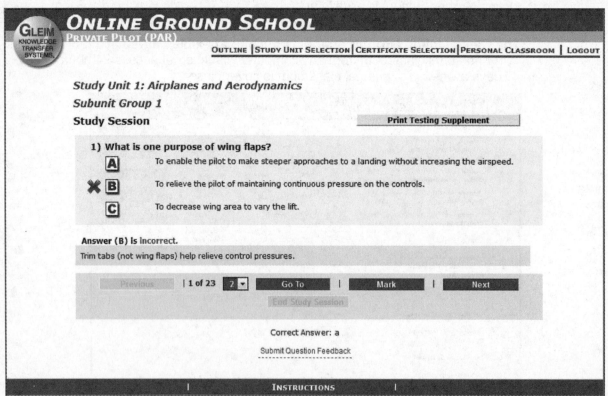

Register for Gleim Online Ground School today: www.GleimAviation.com/OGS

1.11 HELPFUL ORGANIZATIONS

Gleim cooperates with and supports all aspects of the flight training industry, particularly organizations that focus on aviation recruitment, flight training, and advocacy. These include the EAA, AOPA, CAP, WAI, AUVSI, and AMA.

Experimental Aircraft Association: Young Eagles Program

The Experimental Aircraft Association's (EAA) Young Eagles Program set a goal of providing a free introductory flight to 1 million young people ages 8 to 17. They have already exceeded that goal and are still going strong.

The Young Eagles Program is intended to help young people understand the important role aviation plays in our daily lives and, at the same time, provide insight into how an airplane flies, what it takes to become a pilot, and the high standards flying demands in terms of safety and quality.

NOTE: This "Learn to Fly" booklet is used as "ground school" training for Young Eagles programs. For more information about the Young Eagles Program, visit www.youngeagles.org or call 1-877-806-8902.

Aircraft Owners and Pilots Association

The Aircraft Owners and Pilots Association (AOPA) hosts an informational web page on getting started in aviation with information for those still dreaming about flying, those who are ready to begin, and those who are already making the journey.

The goal of this program is to encourage people to experience their dreams of flying through an introductory flight. Interested individuals can order a FREE subscription to Flight Training Magazine, which explains how amazing it is to be a pilot. Other resources are available, such as a flight school finder, a guide on what to expect throughout training, an explanation of pilot certification options, a FREE monthly flight training newsletter, and much more. To learn more, visit www.aopa.org and select the Training and Safety link.

Civil Air Patrol: Cadet Orientation Flight Program

The Civil Air Patrol (CAP) Cadet Orientation Flight Program is designed to introduce CAP cadets to flying. The program is voluntary and primarily motivational, and it is designed to stimulate the cadet's interest in and knowledge of aviation.

Each orientation flight is approximately 1 hour, follows a prescribed syllabus, and is usually in the local area of the airport. Except for takeoff, landing, and a few other portions of the flight, cadets are encouraged to handle the controls.

For more information about the CAP cadet program nearest you, visit the CAP website at www.gocivilairpatrol.com.

Women in Aviation International

Women in Aviation International (WAI) is a nonprofit organization dedicated to the encouragement and advancement of women in all aviation career fields and interests. Its diverse membership includes astronauts, corporate pilots, maintenance technicians, air traffic controllers, business owners, educators, journalists, flight attendants, high school and university students, air show performers, airport managers, and many others.

WAI provides year-round resources to assist women in aviation and to encourage young women to consider aviation as a career. WAI also offers educational outreach programs to educators, aviation industry members, and young people nationally and internationally. An annual Girls in Aviation Day was recently initiated for girls ages 8 to 17.

To learn more about WAI chapters, membership, and outreach programs, visit www.wai.org.

Association for Unmanned Vehicle Systems International

The Association for Unmanned Vehicle Systems International (AUVSI) is the world's largest organization devoted exclusively to advancing the unmanned systems and robotics industries. AUVSI provides its members with a unified voice in advocacy for policies and regulations that encourage growth and innovation. It educates the public and media on the safe and beneficial uses of unmanned systems and enables market growth by offering its members custom resources that can help them realize their full industry potential. AUVSI's Remote Pilots Council also provides local networking for certificated remote pilots and a forum for feedback to the FAA.

Learn more at www.auvsi.org.

Academy of Model Aeronautics

The Academy of Model Aeronautics (AMA) is the world's largest model aviation association, representing a membership of more than 195,000 people from every walk of life, income level, and age group. The purpose of this self-supporting, non-profit organization is to promote the development of model aviation as a recognized sport and recreation activity. It is the official national body for model aviation in the United States.

The AMA sanctions more than 2,000 model competitions throughout the country each year and certifies official model flying records on a national and international level. It organizes the annual National Aeromodeling Championships, the world's largest model airplane competition. The AMA is the chartering organization for more than 2,500 model airplane clubs across the country, offering its chartered clubs official contest sanction, insurance, and assistance in acquiring and maintaining flying sites.

Membership is open to anyone interested in model aviation. Consider joining the AMA today at www.modelaircraft.org.

1.12 AVIATION CAREER OPPORTUNITIES

Many people approach aviation as a hobby: something they do for fun or for personal travel flexibility. Still others look at aviation as an industry in which they would like to work and earn their living. You might think the only job opportunity in aviation is a commercial airline pilot. While this is certainly a prestigious career, there are many other opportunities in aviation. This section will introduce you to a few of those opportunities and give you insight into what is involved in each.

Commercial Airline Pilot

As this is the most obvious aviation job, we'll start with it. Commercial airline pilots all start exactly where you are now, thinking about aviation and dreaming of getting into the cockpit. It all starts with that first flight lesson. From there, you will need to obtain several certifications from the FAA and build up a wealth of flight time and experience flying various aircraft for various purposes. Airlines like well-rounded candidates with lots of varied flight experience. The airline interview hiring process is complex and difficult, as it should be. You will have to prove your skills in a classroom setting and in a flight simulator, where you will need to pass a check flight. After that is completed, you will become a first officer and gain valuable experience from your captain. Once you have enough seniority, you can upgrade to captain and provide that mentorship to someone else. Being a commercial airline pilot is a rewarding career that carries a great deal of responsibility. Your office will have the best view imaginable!

Flight Educator

This is not necessarily limited to just being a flight instructor, one who teaches people to fly. A flight educator could be a senior instructor at a flight school, responsible for managing other instructors; a flight school administrator; a professor/teacher at an aviation college, high school, or academy; or any other number of positions where flight students are being educated on how to become or remain pilots. This position is vitally important to the aviation ecosystem, because without flight educators, there will be no pilots. This segment of aviation is directly responsible for creating the next generation of pilots and keeping the current pilots flying.

Aviation Maintenance Technician

Aviation maintenance technicians (AMTs) keep all of our aircraft flying -- and not just flying, but flying safely. This is another vital segment of the aviation industry that is often overlooked by people seeking to enter aviation as a career, but it is one with incredible opportunities. AMTs work on small, general aviation aircraft; commercial airlines; and everything in between. Most AMTs specialize in a certain segment of aviation maintenance, like fabric restoration (yes, there are still tons of fabric-covered airplanes flying around), rotorcraft, aircraft engines, sheet metal repairs, avionics (cockpit systems), or any of 100+ other specialties. There are schools all over the country that train and certify AMTs.

Like being a pilot, AMT training is intensive, and the work carries with it a huge responsibility. However, that responsibility also yields a huge reward as you watch an aircraft you repaired take off and fly to its destination.

Other Opportunities

There are many more aviation career opportunities that we can't fully detail here, but hopefully this introduction to the topic will inspire you to pursue aviation as a career or, at the very least, search out additional opportunities that might interest you. The aviation industry is an exciting industry, and we want you to find a place in it.

INTRODUCTORY FLIGHT

An introductory flight is an amazing opportunity for you to experience flying. Most flight schools and instructors charge a reduced rate for an introductory flight. Just call a local flight school and give it a shot. You will find that flying is not as difficult as you previously thought and it's a lot more fun!

We suggest that you request an early morning or late afternoon flight with the objective of flying in smooth air, which will be more enjoyable to you. Windy conditions will make your flight bumpy. Reschedule if appropriate to ensure a very positive experience and maximum enjoyment.

Congratulations! You are taking the first big step toward learning to fly by scheduling

1. Your introductory flight with a local flight school,
2. Your Young Eagle airplane ride with the Experimental Aircraft Association,
3. Your first Cadet Orientation Flight with the Civil Air Patrol, or
4. Your first lesson or other flight.

Once your flight is scheduled, what should you expect? Fun, excitement, and the thrill of flying, of course!

You will meet your instructor (or pilot), and if this is an introductory flight, your instructor will probably take you directly to the airplane you will be flying after a short briefing of what to expect. When you arrive at your airplane on an introductory flight, your instructor will perform the preflight inspection and answer any of your questions. On your first flight lesson, you will do the preflight inspection along with your instructor. During your first few flight lessons, your instructor will go into great detail about what to inspect – with the goal of forming the same habit in you.

When the airplane passes the preflight check, you will get into the airplane with your instructor, who will help you adjust your seat properly and explain the flight controls and the instruments. Fasten your safety belt and shoulder harness before beginning the procedure to start the engine and taxi out to the runway. Notice your instructor is using a checklist to ensure that all of the steps are done in a logical order and that the airplane is safe to fly.

Your instructor may let you taxi the airplane, which you steer with your feet by pressing the rudder pedals.

As all of this is happening, you may say to yourself, "This is great, but how will I ever learn to do all of this?" Remember that, at one time, your flight instructor, airline pilots, and even astronauts were sitting where you are now. This is a new experience and it is natural to feel overwhelmed. You will not be expected to know everything at the beginning.

After all of the checks have been done, your instructor will assure you that the airplane is ready for takeoff. This is why you are here! Your instructor will taxi the airplane out onto the runway, line it up with the centerline, and move the throttle to full power. Most instructors will have you keep a hand on the control yoke and both feet on the pedals. You follow your instructor's movements on the controls, but the instructor is flying the airplane.

   LIFTOFF! Now you are flying! That seemed pretty easy, and as the airplane climbs higher, the view is breathtaking. Your instructor will inform you that you have the controls. This means that you are now flying the airplane. Your instructor will demonstrate how to fly straight-and-level, make turns, and climb and descend. These maneuvers are briefly described here and explained in more detail on pages 27 through 32.

A. **Level flight** means flying at a constant altitude by keeping a reference point, like the airplane's nose, in a fixed position relative to the horizon.

   1. The altimeter is an instrument that measures altitude and is used to determine whether level flight is being maintained.

      a. If altitude is being lost or gained, the nose of the airplane should be moved up or down in relation to the horizon, and then the altimeter should be checked to determine if altitude is being maintained.

   2. Pulling back or pushing forward on the control yoke moves the nose up or down.

      a. The control yoke is also called a control wheel or control stick. In some airplanes, it is a stick that can be moved right or left and forward or back.

B. **Straight flight** means flying on a constant heading, or direction. You should form an imaginary line by selecting two or more reference points, like roads, towns, or lakes, that are directly ahead of the airplane. Then keep the airplane headed along that line.

   1. The wings should be kept level by using the ailerons. The ailerons are controlled by turning the control yoke left or right.

C. To **turn** the airplane, you must turn the control yoke, or wheel, while pressing the appropriate rudder pedal with your foot. In other words, to turn left, you must turn the control wheel to the left and press the left rudder.

   1. To come out of a turn, you must turn the control wheel in the opposite direction and press the opposite rudder. In other words, to roll the wings level while turning to the left, you must turn the control wheel to the right and press the right rudder.

   2. These control pressures should be gradually and smoothly released as the wings become level and the airplane again enters straight-and-level flight.

D. **Climbs.** To cause the airplane to climb, you must pull back on the control yoke and adjust the throttle to increase the power.

1. To level off from a climb, lower the nose of the airplane by gradually pushing forward on the control yoke.

2. When the airspeed reaches the desired speed, reduce the throttle setting to the appropriate power setting.

E. **Descents.** The airplane loses altitude in a controlled manner. Reduce power with the throttle and lower the nose by pushing the control yoke forward to maintain the desired airspeed.

1. To end the descent, you should raise the nose to a level attitude and, at the same time, increase power to the desired throttle setting.

After 15 to 20 minutes, your instructor will inform you that it is time to return to the airport. Your instructor will perform the landing and explain what is happening. As you exit from the runway, your instructor may let you have another try at taxiing the airplane.

Once the airplane is parked and secured and you have all your belongings, your instructor will answer your questions regarding your flight and how to begin flying lessons. You may also be able to schedule your first flight lesson. See pages 2 through 8 for a complete discussion of how to proceed.

2.1 COST TO OBTAIN YOUR PILOT CERTIFICATES

The price of instruction varies nationwide and also from flight school to flight school. Fuel, maintenance, and airplane expenses play a major role in determining airplane rental rates. Shop around to make sure you are buying what you want at a fair price. Your total cost will depend on the FBO, equipment, local cost factors, competition, etc., and the amount of training you require in excess of the minimum flight hour requirement (20 for sport and 40 for private). Many flight schools allow payments lesson by lesson rather than all at once. Some flight schools offer discounts for purchasing a block of flight time.

SPORT PILOT CERTIFICATE		PRIVATE PILOT CERTIFICATE	
Medical Exam	$ N/A	Medical Exam	$ 90
Books and Supplies	300	Books and Supplies	350
Gleim kit		Gleim kit	
Aeronautical sectional chart		Aeronautical sectional chart	
Chart Supplement		Chart Supplement	
Airplane information manual		Airplane information manual	
Knowledge Test Fee	150	Knowledge Test Fee	150
15 hr. of Dual	2,025	30 hr. of Dual	4,800
($95/hr. aircraft + $40/hr. instructor)		($120/hr. aircraft + $40/hr. instructor)	
5 hr. of Solo	475	10 hr. of Solo	1,200
($95/hr. for aircraft)		($120/hr. for aircraft)	
Rental of Aircraft for Flight Test	190	Rental of Aircraft for Flight Test	300
Practical Test Fee	350	Practical Test Fee	350
TOTAL	$3,490	TOTAL	$7,240

Note this is the **low end** of the cost range. For private certificates, most pilots require 55 hours or more. Also, aircraft rental can range from $55 to $180 per hr. or more, depending on the airplane, age, type, and equipment installed. (Age of the aircraft does not imply less reliability.)

The private certificate costs between $8,000 and $12,000 on average.

The Gleim *Private Pilot Syllabus* will assist you and your CFI in completing your training in less than 55 hours!

2.2 TIME REQUIRED TO OBTAIN YOUR PILOT CERTIFICATES

While only 20 hours of *flight* time is required for the sport pilot certificate and 40 hours of *flight* time is required for the private pilot certificate, the *total* process usually takes several months and hundreds of hours due to commuting, ground training, aircraft preflight, canceled lessons due to bad weather, airplane maintenance, etc. Expect the sport pilot certificate to take half the amount of time as the private pilot certificate would take.

A typical chronological order of flying time follows. The numbers on the left are the minimum using our **Private Pilot Syllabus** under Part 61.

```
14.5 to  17 hr.  -  Presolo (dual)
 2.0 to   5 hr.  -  Solo
 5.0 to   7 hr.  -  Precross-country (dual)
 5.5 to   9 hr.  -  Cross-country and night flying (dual)
 7.0 to   8 hr.  -  Cross-country (solo)
 7.0 to  10 hr.  -  Preparation for practical (flight) test (dual and solo)
41.0 to  56
```

Your sport pilot certificate can be obtained in as little as 2 weeks (1 month for private) with near full-time effort. A more realistic timetable is 1 to 2 months for sport and 3 to 4 months for private. The ideal situation is to fly **at least** once or twice per week to maintain a higher level of proficiency.

2.3 SCHEDULING A VISIT TO YOUR LOCAL AIRPORT

With all this information in mind, you have a solid, basic grasp of what is going on at your local airport. Now it's time to set up a visit! The information below will help you arrange and organize your visit.

Step 1: Find a local airport to tour.

- Use the Gleim Airport Search Tool (available under Resources at www.GleimAviation.com) to search for and gather information about airports near you.
- Print out airport information pages for each airport you intend to visit.

Step 2: Contact the airport and set up a time to visit.

- Call the airport manager at the phone number listed on the airport information page.
- Explain who you are and that you are interested in learning more about aviation.
- Inform the airport manager that you would like to take a tour of the airport.
- Set up a convenient time to go to the airport.

Step 3: Arrive at the airport on time and take your tour.

- Don't be late. Arrive on time.
- Carry your course information in a binder for easy reference.
- Introduce yourself in the airport office and explain that you have arrived for your tour of the airport.
- Answer any security questions the airport employee asks you; then follow your escort's instructions as you move outside to take a tour.
- While on your tour, ask questions to gain a better understanding of what is going on at the airport.

Step 4: Thank your escort for his or her time and assistance.

- Be courteous and thank your escort for showing you around and answering your questions.
- Ask if there is a place you can sit to observe air traffic. If there is, sit down and enjoy the view.

Step 5: Find another local airport and repeat the process.

- After you return home from your first airport visit, you may find that you are more excited than ever to get more involved in aviation. You've done this once; now you can do it again and again!
- The more airports you visit, the better understanding you will have of how general aviation works and how you might be able to become a part of the excitement.

AIRPLANES: HOW THEY FLY

The purpose of the next seven pages is to introduce you to the parts of the airplane and to aerodynamics, i.e., the forces acting on the airplane in flight. Remember, this is technical material that will make more sense as you begin your flight lessons.

3.1 THE AIRPLANE

The first figure below is a high-wing aircraft, such as a Cessna 152. On low-wing airplanes, such as the Beech Skipper and the Piper Tomahawk, the wings are affixed to the bottom rather than the top of the fuselage, as indicated in the second figure below.

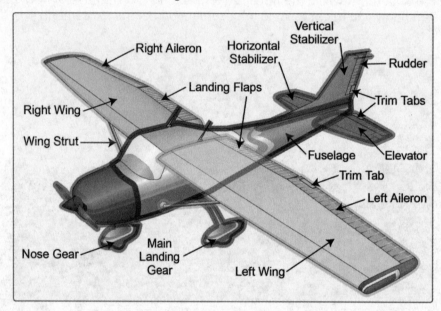

1. ***Wing*** -- Provides lift by creating a low pressure area on the top of the wing and a high pressure area on the bottom. The top of the wing is curved, which provides a longer distance for air to flow over the wing than under the wing. As the air on top of the wing travels a greater distance in the same amount of time, it moves faster than the air flowing under the wing, which results in less pressure on top than on the bottom of the wing. At the same time, the bottom of the wing deflects air downward, which also produces lift.

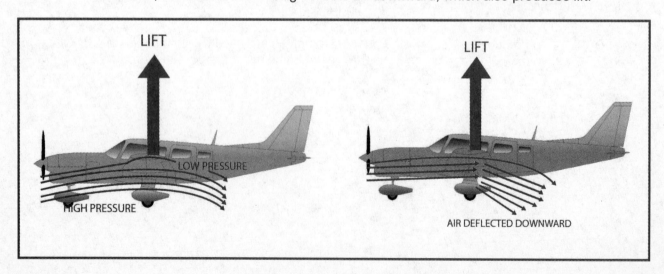

2. ***Fuselage*** -- The main component of the airplane. Its function is to act as a carrier for the wings and tail section. It also is designed to produce a limited amount of lift.

3. ***Horizontal stabilizer*** -- This structure, located in the rear of the airplane, is designed to provide continuous longitudinal (from front to rear) stability. It prevents uncontrolled up and down movements of the nose (pitching).

4. ***Elevator*** -- A movable part on the rear of the horizontal stabilizer. It is used to move the airplane about the lateral axis. It provides the input of pitch and helps control altitude. Note the axes of rotation are discussed and illustrated on page 24.

5. ***Vertical stabilizer*** -- This surface provides directional (right or left) stability. It acts like a weathervane. It prevents uncontrolled left or right movements of the nose (yawing).

6. ***Rudder*** -- This surface, which is connected to the vertical stabilizer, moves the airplane around its vertical axis and is used to yaw (move the tail to the left or right) the airplane.

7. ***Rudder and elevator trim tabs*** -- These small, movable surfaces decrease control pressures and help to establish hands-off flight (i.e., when the airplane will almost fly by itself). All airplanes have elevator trim tabs controlled from the cockpit.

8. ***Right and left ailerons*** -- These surfaces, located on the outside trailing edges of the wings, control the airplane around its longitudinal axis, i.e., the degree of bank, or whether one wing is higher or lower than the other wing (rolling).

9. ***Aileron trim tab*** -- This small movable section of one or both ailerons permits adjustment so the wings remain level; i.e., you can compensate for more weight on either side of the airplane. Not all airplanes have aileron trim tabs.

10. ***Flaps*** -- These surfaces are located on the inside trailing edges of the wings. They can be extended to provide greater wing area at slower speeds. This provides more lift and drag and allows an airplane to land, take off, or fly at slower speeds.

11. ***Main landing gear*** -- The component of the airplane that touches the runway first during a normal landing. It is designed to take large loads and impacts.

12. ***Nose gear*** -- This component is designed to steer the airplane on the ground. It is not designed for excessive impacts or loads. However, it is designed to carry the weight of the forward portion of the airplane.

13. ***Nosewheel* (tricycle) vs. *tailwheel* (conventional)** -- Nosewheel airplanes have the "third" wheel in front of the main landing gear (i.e., under the nose), as pictured below. Nosewheel airplanes have much better handling (because there is less airplane behind the pivot point) and visibility characteristics while taxiing. Almost all new airplanes are nosewheel design.

    a. Tailwheel airplanes have the "third" wheel under the tail. Tailwheel airplanes can land on much rougher terrain and, consequently, are used by bush pilots. In a tailwheel airplane, this gear supports the weight of the rear portion of the airplane.

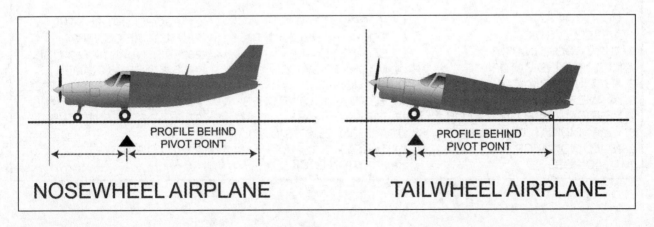

NOSEWHEEL AIRPLANE   TAILWHEEL AIRPLANE

14. ***Retractable landing gear*** -- Retracting the gear reduces drag and increases airspeed without the need for additional power. The landing gear normally retracts into the wing or fuselage through an opening, which may be covered by doors after the gear is retracted. The smooth door will provide for the unrestricted flow of air across the opening that houses the gear. The retraction or extension of the landing gear is accomplished either electrically or hydraulically by landing gear controls from within the cockpit. Warning indicators are usually provided in the cockpit to indicate whether the wheels are extended and locked or retracted. In nearly all airplanes equipped with retractable landing gear, a system is provided for emergency gear extension in the event landing gear mechanisms fail to lower the gear.

3.2   INSIDE THE AIRPLANE

The following is a diagram of a Cessna instrument panel. It may contain more equipment than is found in some trainer-type airplanes used by student pilots.

1. CLOCK
2. AIRSPEED INDICATOR
3. TURN COORDINATOR
4. ATTITUDE INDICATOR
5. HEADING INDICATOR
6. ALTIMETER
7. VERTICAL SPEED INDICATOR (VSI)
8. NAV 1 INDICATOR
9. NAV 2 INDICATOR
10. AVIONICS

11. HOBBS METER
12. TEMPERATURE CONTROL
13. CONTROL YOKE
14. MAGNETO SWITCH
15. TACHOMETER
16. ELECTRICAL SWITCHES
17. PARKING BRAKE
18. ALTERNATE STATIC SOURCE
19. THROTTLE
20. FRICTION LOCK

21. PROPELLER CONTROL
22. MIXTURE CONTROL
23. FUEL QUANTITY GAUGES
24. ENGINE INSTRUMENTS
25. LIGHT DIMMER CONTROLS
26. CIRCUIT BREAKER PANEL
27. FLAP CONTROL LEVER
28. GPS
29. AUTO PILOT

3.3 CATEGORIES OF AIRCRAFT

The seven categories of aircraft and their subdivision into classes are listed below.

1. ***Airplanes***

     a.　Single-engine land
     b.　Multi-engine land
     c.　Single-engine sea
     d.　Multi-engine sea

2. ***Gliders***

3. ***Rotorcraft***

     a.　Gyroplane -- Thrust provided by pusher propeller and lift by unpowered rotorblade.
     b.　Helicopter -- Rotorblade is powered to obtain lift and thrust.

4. ***Lighter-than-air***

     a.　Airship
     b.　Gas balloon
     c.　Hot air balloon

5. ***Powered lift***

6. ***Powered parachute***

     a.　Land
     b.　Sea

7. ***Weight-shift-control***

     a.　Land
     b.　Sea

3.4 AXES OF ROTATION

A. The airplane has three axes of rotation around which it moves, as seen in the illustration below.

    1. *Lateral (pitch) axis* -- an imaginary line from wingtip to wingtip

        a. Rotation about the lateral axis is called **pitch** and is controlled by the elevator.

        b. The rotation is similar to a seesaw. The bar holding the seesaw is the lateral axis.

        c. The angle between the airplane's nose and the horizon is known as the airplane's **pitch attitude**.

    2. *Longitudinal (roll) axis* -- an imaginary line from the nose to the tail

        a. Rotation about the longitudinal axis is called **roll** and is controlled by the ailerons.

        b. The rotation is similar to a barbecue rotisserie, in which the spit is the longitudinal axis.

        c. The angle between the airplane's wings and the horizon is known as the airplane's bank.

    3. *Vertical (yaw) axis* -- an imaginary line extending vertically through the intersection of the lateral and longitudinal axes

        a. Rotation about the vertical axis is called **yaw** and is controlled by the rudder. This rotation is referred to as directional control or directional stability.

        b. The rotation is similar to a weather vane, in which the post holding the vane is the vertical axis.

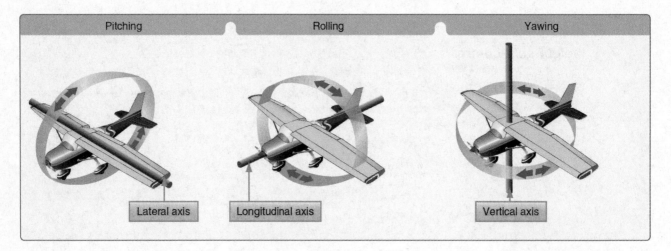

B. The airplane can rotate around one, two, or all three axes simultaneously. Think of these axes as imaginary axles around which the airplane turns, much as a wheel would turn around axles positioned in these same three directions.

3.5 FLIGHT CONTROLS AND CONTROL SURFACES

A. *Primary Flight Controls.* The airplane is controlled by deflection of flight control surfaces. These are hinged or movable surfaces with which the pilot adjusts the airplane's attitude during takeoff, flight maneuvering, and landing (airplane attitude refers to whether the airplane is pointing up, down, etc.). The flight control surfaces are operated by the pilot through connecting linkage to the rudder pedals and a control yoke.

    1. The **control yoke** is similar to the steering wheel of a car. However, you can push and pull it in addition to turning it. The push/pull movement controls the third dimension in which airplanes move (up and down). Remember, a car can only go straight or turn (move in two dimensions), but an airplane can go straight, turn, or move up and down.

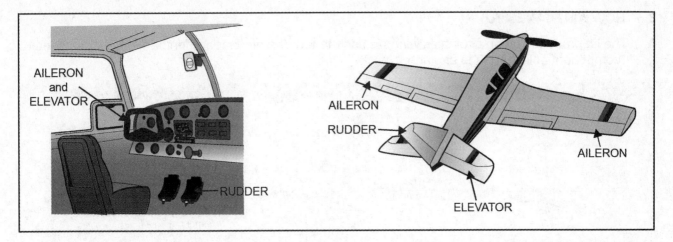

2.   The **rudder** is attached to the vertical stabilizer. Controlled by the rudder pedals, the rudder is used by the pilot to control the direction (left or right) of yaw about the airplane's vertical axis for minor adjustments. It is NOT used to make the airplane turn, as is often erroneously believed. Banking the airplane makes it turn. See "How Airplanes Turn" on the following page.

3.   The **elevators** are attached to the horizontal stabilizer. The elevators provide the pilot with control of the pitch attitude about the airplane's lateral axis. The elevators are controlled by pushing or pulling the control yoke.

4.   The outboard movable portions of each wing are the **ailerons**. The term "aileron" means "little wing" in French. Ailerons are located on the trailing (rear) edge of each wing near the outer tips. When deflected up or down, they in effect change the wing's camber (curvature) and its angle of attack. This changes the wing's lift and drag characteristics.

   a.   Their primary use is to bank (roll) the airplane around its longitudinal axis. The banking of the wings results in the airplane turning in the direction of the bank, i.e., toward the direction of the low wing.

   b.   The ailerons are interconnected in the control system to operate simultaneously in opposite directions of each other. As the aileron on one wing is deflected downward, the aileron on the opposite wing is deflected upward.

   c.   The ailerons are controlled by turning the control yoke.

B.   *Secondary Flight Controls.* In addition to primary flight controls, most airplanes have another group called secondary controls. These include trim devices of various types and wing flaps.

   1.   **Trim tabs** are commonly used to relieve the pilot from maintaining continuous pressure on the primary controls when correcting for an unbalanced flight condition caused by changes in aerodynamic forces or weight.

   2.   **Wing flaps** are installed on the wings of most airplanes. Flaps increase both lift and drag and have three important functions:

      a.   First, they permit a slower landing speed, which decreases the required landing distance.

      b.   Second, they permit a comparatively steep angle of descent without an increase in speed. This makes it possible to safely clear obstacles when making a landing approach to a small field.

      c.   Third, they may also be used to shorten the takeoff distance and provide a steeper climb path.

3.6 HOW AIRPLANES TURN

A.   The lift produced by an airplane's wings is used to turn the airplane. When banked, the horizontal component of lift turns the airplane.

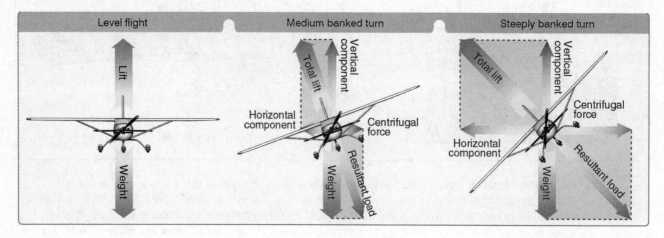

1.   Until a force acts on the airplane, it tends to fly straight ahead due to inertia.

   a.   Inertia is the phenomenon observed when moving objects continue to move in the same direction; i.e., they tend not to turn unless acted upon by an outside force.

2.   When the airplane begins to turn, centrifugal force pulls the airplane away from the turn, i.e., tends to make it fly straight ahead.

3.   The horizontal component of lift (in a bank) counteracts the centrifugal force.

   a.   Therefore, the greater the bank, the sharper the turn or the greater the rate of turn because more of the total lift goes into the horizontal component.

4.   The rudder does not turn the airplane. It controls the yaw about the vertical axis.

   a.   This permits the "coordination" of the rudder and ailerons.

   b.   **Coordinated flight** is when the airplane goes "straight ahead" through the relative wind.

B.   In a bank, the total lift consists of both horizontal lift (counteracting centrifugal force) and vertical lift (counteracting weight and gravity).

1.   Therefore, given the same amount of total lift, there is less vertical lift in a bank than in straight-and-level flight.

2.   Thus, to maintain altitude in a turn, you must

   a.   Increase back pressure on the control yoke (for a higher angle of attack to produce more lift), and/or

   b.   Increase power.

C.   The turn is stopped by decreasing the bank to zero (i.e., wings level).

BASIC FLIGHT MANEUVERS

In this section, we will provide you with more detailed information on the basic flight maneuvers (straight-and-level, turns, climbs, and descents). Do not feel overwhelmed. Just read and try to understand the basic concepts. Write down questions to ask your instructor. At the beginning of each flight lesson, your instructor will sit down with you to go over what you will do during the lesson. This is called a preflight briefing. It is a discussion between you and your CFI that should answer all of your questions. Your home study before the lesson will reduce the time spent on the preflight briefing and provide you with quality flight training time -- all of which keeps costs down.

4.1 FLIGHT INSTRUMENTS

A.   When you are sitting in the airplane, you will probably notice six flight instruments in front of you. The typical arrangement of these instruments is shown below.

1.   The airspeed indicator (ASI) displays the speed at which the airplane is moving through the air. The ASI in the figure is indicating an airspeed of 84 knots.

2.   The attitude indicator (AI) displays the attitude of the airplane (nose up, nose down, wings banked) in relation to the horizon. The AI in the figure is indicating a climbing right turn.

> Sport Pilots: You may not have all six flight instruments. At a minimum, you will have
>
> 1.   Airspeed indicator
> 2.   Altimeter
> 3.   Compass to determine direction in lieu of a heading indicator

3. The altimeter (ALT) displays the altitude of the airplane above mean sea level (MSL) when properly adjusted to the current pressure setting. The ALT in the figure is indicating an altitude of 4,900 ft. MSL.

4. The turn coordinator (TC) displays the rate at which a turn is being made. The miniature airplane banks in the direction of the turn. At the bottom of the instrument is a ball in a glass tube called an inclinometer. The inclinometer indicates whether the airplane is in coordinated flight (ball centered) or uncoordinated flight. The TC in the figure is indicating a right turn and uncoordinated flight.

5. The heading indicator (HI) displays the heading (direction) the airplane is flying. The HI in the figure is indicating a heading of 250°.

6. The vertical speed indicator (VSI) displays whether the airplane is in level flight, climbing, or descending. The rate of climb or descent is indicated in hundreds of feet per minute. The VSI in the figure indicates a climb at 700 feet per minute.

4.2 AIRPLANE CONTROL

A. Airplane control is composed of three components: pitch control, bank control, and power control.

1. **Pitch control** is the control of the airplane about its lateral axis (i.e., wingtip to wingtip) by applying elevator pressure to raise or lower the nose, usually in relation to the horizon.

2. **Bank control** is the control of the airplane about its longitudinal axis (i.e., nose to tail) by use of the ailerons to attain the desired angle of bank in relation to the horizon.

3. **Power control** is the control of power or thrust by use of the throttle to establish or maintain a desired airspeed, climb rate, or descent rate in coordination with the attitude changes.

For additional information on the flight controls and control surfaces, see page 24.

B. The objectives of the basic flight maneuvers are

1. To learn the proper use of the flight controls for maneuvering the airplane

2. To attain the proper attitude in relation to the horizon by use of visual and instrument references

3. To emphasize the importance of dividing your attention and constantly checking all reference points while looking for other traffic

4.3 STRAIGHT-AND-LEVEL FLIGHT

A. Straight-and-level flight means that a constant heading and altitude are maintained.

1. It is accomplished by making corrections for deviations in direction and altitude from unintentional turns, descents, and climbs.

B. The pitch attitude for **level flight** (i.e., constant altitude) is obtained by selecting some portion of the airplane's nose or instrument glare shield as a reference point and then keeping that point in a fixed position relative to the horizon.

1. That position should be cross-checked occasionally against the altimeter to determine whether or not the pitch attitude is correct for the power setting being used.

a. If altitude is being lost or gained, the pitch attitude should be readjusted in relation to the horizon, and then the altimeter should be checked to determine if altitude is being maintained.

2. The application of forward or back elevator pressure is used to control this attitude.

3. The pitch information obtained from the attitude indicator also shows the position of the nose relative to the horizon.

C. To achieve **straight flight** (i.e., constant heading), you should select two or more outside visual reference points directly ahead of the airplane (e.g., roads, section lines, towns, lakes, etc.) to form an imaginary line and then keep the airplane headed along that line.

    1. While using these references, you should occasionally check the heading indicator (HI) to determine that the airplane is maintaining a constant heading.

    2. Both wingtips should be equidistant above or below the horizon (depending on whether your airplane is a high-wing or low-wing type). Any necessary adjustment should be made with the ailerons to return to a wings level flight attitude.

    3. The attitude indicator (AI) should be checked for small bank angles, and the heading indicator (HI) should be checked to note deviations from the desired direction.

D. Straight-and-level flight requires almost no application of control pressure if the airplane is properly trimmed and the air is smooth.

    1. Trim the airplane so it will fly straight and level without constant assistance.

        a. This is called "hands-off flight."

        b. Improper trim technique usually results in flying that is physically tiring, particularly in prolonged straight-and-level flight.

    2. The airplane should be trimmed by first applying control pressure to establish the desired attitude and then adjusting the trim so that the airplane will maintain that attitude without control pressure in hands-off flight.

E. The airspeed will remain constant in straight-and-level flight with a constant power setting.

    1. Significant changes in airspeed (e.g., power changes) will require considerable changes in pitch attitude to maintain altitude.

    2. Pronounced changes in pitch attitude will also be necessary as the flaps and landing gear (if retractable) are operated.

4.4 TURNS

A. A turn is a basic flight maneuver used to change from, or return to, a desired heading. This maneuver involves the coordinated use of the ailerons, rudder, and elevator.

B. To enter a turn, you should simultaneously turn the control wheel (i.e., apply aileron control pressure) and apply rudder pressure in the desired direction.

    1. The speed (or rate) at which your airplane rolls into a bank depends on the rate and amount of control pressure you apply.

Slipping turn

        a. The amount of bank depends on how long you keep the ailerons deflected.

    2. Rudder pressure must be enough to keep the ball of the inclinometer (part of the turn coordinator) centered.

        a. If the ball is not centered, "step on the ball" to recenter it.

        b. EXAMPLE: If the ball is to the right, apply right rudder pressure (i.e., step on the ball) to recenter it.

3. The best outside reference for establishing the degree of bank is the angle made by the top of the engine cowling or the instrument panel with respect to the horizon.

  a. Since on most light airplanes the engine cowling is fairly flat, its angle relative to the horizon will give some indication of the approximate degree of bank.

4. Information obtained from the attitude indicator (AI) will show the angle of the wings in relation to the horizon. Referring to this information will help you learn to judge the degree of bank based on outside references.

C. The lift produced by the wings is used to turn the airplane, as discussed in "How Airplanes Turn" on page 26.

1. To maintain a constant altitude, you will need to apply enough back elevator pressure (i.e., raise the nose of the airplane in order to increase the angle of attack) to prevent a descent.

D. As the desired angle of bank is established, aileron and rudder pressures should be released. The bank will not continue to increase since the aileron control surfaces will be neutral in their streamlined position.

1. The back elevator pressure should not be released but should be held constant or sometimes increased to maintain a constant altitude.

2. Throughout the turn, you should cross-check the outside references and occasionally include the altimeter to determine whether the pitch attitude is correct.

3. If you are gaining or losing altitude, adjust the pitch attitude in relation to the horizon, and then recheck the altimeter and vertical speed indicator to determine if altitude is now being maintained.

E. The roll-out from a turn to straight flight is similar to the roll-in to the turn from straight flight except that control pressures are used in the opposite direction. Aileron and rudder pressures are applied in the direction of the roll-out (i.e., toward the high wing).

1. As the angle of bank decreases, the elevator pressure should be released smoothly as necessary to maintain altitude. Remember, when the airplane is no longer banked, the vertical component of lift increases.

2. Since the airplane will continue turning as long as there is any bank, the roll-out must be started before reaching the desired heading.

  a. The time the roll-out should begin, in order to lead the desired heading, will depend on the rate of turn and the rate at which the roll-out will be made.

3. As the wings become level, the control pressures should be gradually and smoothly released so that the controls are neutralized as the airplane resumes straight-and-level flight.

4. As the roll-out is completed, attention should be given to outside visual references as well as to the attitude indicator and heading indicator to determine that the wings are leveled precisely and that the turn is stopped.

4.5 CLIMBS

A. Climbs and climbing turns are basic flight maneuvers in which the pitch attitude and power setting result in a gain in altitude. In a straight climb, the airplane gains altitude while traveling straight ahead. In climbing turns, the airplane gains altitude while turning.

B. To enter the climb, simultaneously advance the throttle and apply back elevator pressure.

1. As the power is increased to the climb setting, the airplane's nose will tend to rise to the climb attitude.

  a. In most trainer-type airplanes, the climb setting will be full power.

2. While the pitch attitude increases and airspeed decreases, progressively more right-rudder pressure must be used to compensate for torque effects and to maintain direction.

    a. Because the angle of attack is relatively high, the airspeed is relatively slow, and the power setting is high, the airplane will have a tendency to roll and yaw to the left due to turning tendencies created by the rotating propeller.

        1) While right-rudder pressure will correct for the yaw, some aileron pressure may also be required to keep the wings level.

C. When the climb is established, back elevator pressure must be maintained to keep the pitch attitude constant.

    1. As the airspeed decreases, the elevators may try to return to their streamlined or neutral position, which will cause the nose to lower.

        a. Nose-up trim will therefore be required.

    2. You will need to cross-check the airspeed indicator (ASI) because you want to climb at a specific airspeed and because the ASI will provide an indirect indication of the pitch attitude.

        a. If the airspeed is higher than desired, you need to raise the nose.

        b. If the airspeed is lower than desired, you need to lower the nose.

    3. After the climbing attitude, power setting, and airspeed have been established, trim the airplane to relieve all pressures from the controls.

        a. If further adjustments are made in pitch, power, and/or airspeed, you must retrim the airplane.

    4. If a straight climb is being performed, you need to maintain a constant heading with the wings level.

        a. If a climbing turn is being performed, maintain a constant angle of bank.

D. To return to straight-and-level flight from a climbing attitude, you should start the level-off below the desired altitude in order to avoid climbing through it.

    1. To level off, the nose should be lowered.

    2. The nose must be lowered gradually, however, because a loss of altitude will result if the pitch attitude is decreased too abruptly before allowing the airspeed to increase adequately.

        a. As the nose is lowered, retrim the airplane.

        b. When the airspeed reaches the desired cruise speed, reduce the throttle setting to appropriate cruise power setting and trim the airplane.

E. **Climbing Turns.** The following factors should be considered:

    1. With a constant power setting, the same pitch attitude and airspeed cannot be maintained in a bank as in a straight climb due to the decrease in the vertical lift and airspeed during a turn.

Climbing left bank

        a. The loss of vertical lift becomes greater as the angle of bank is increased, so shallow turns may be used to maintain an efficient rate of climb. If a medium- or steep-banked turn is used, the airplane's rate of climb will be reduced.

        b. The airplane will have a greater tendency towards nose heaviness than in a straight climb, due to the decrease of vertical lift.

    2. As in all maneuvers, attention should be divided among all references equally.

F.   There are two ways to establish a climbing turn: either establish a straight climb and then turn or establish the pitch and bank attitudes simultaneously from straight-and-level flight.

   1.   The second method is usually preferred because you can more effectively check the area for other aircraft while the climb is being established.

4.6 DESCENTS

A.   A descent is a basic maneuver in which the airplane loses altitude in a controlled manner. Descents can be made

   1.   With partial power, as used during an approach to a landing
   2.   Without power, i.e., as a glide
   3.   At cruise airspeeds, during en route descents

B.   To enter a descent, you should first apply carburetor heat (if recommended by the manufacturer) and then reduce power to the desired setting or to idle.

   1.   Maintain a constant altitude by applying back elevator pressure as required until the airspeed decreases to the desired descent airspeed.

   2.   Once the descent airspeed has been reached, lower the pitch attitude to maintain that airspeed and adjust the trim.

C.   When the descent is established, cross-check the airspeed indicator (ASI) to ensure that you are descending at the desired airspeed.

   1.   If the airspeed is higher than desired, slightly raise the nose and allow the airspeed to stabilize in order to confirm the adjustment.

   2.   If the airspeed is lower than desired, slightly lower the nose and allow the airspeed to stabilize.

   3.   Once you are descending at the desired airspeed, note the position of the airplane's nose relative to the horizon and the indications of the attitude indicator (AI).

      a.   Trim the airplane to relieve all control pressures.

   4.   Maintain either straight or turning flight, as desired.

D.   The level-off from a descent must be started before reaching the desired altitude in order to avoid descending through it.

   1.   To level off, you should simultaneously raise the nose to a level attitude and increase power to the desired cruise setting.

      a.   The addition of power and the increase in airspeed will tend to raise the nose. You will need to apply appropriate elevator control pressure and make a trim adjustment to relieve the control pressures.

E.   **Turning Descents**

   1.   As with climbing turns, you can either enter the turn after the descent has been established or simultaneously adjust the bank and pitch attitudes.

   2.   At a desired power setting during a descending turn, maintain airspeed with pitch as you would in a straight descent.

ADVANCED PILOT TRAINING

5.1 THE INSTRUMENT RATING

An instrument rating is added to your private or commercial pilot certificate upon satisfactory completion of your training program, a pilot knowledge test, and a practical test. Your private or commercial pilot certificate will look the same, except it will have the words "Instrument Airplane" typed on the certificate under the ratings section.

As the title implies, an instrument rating permits you to fly "by instruments," i.e., without visual references to the ground, horizon, and other landmarks. You will be able to fly through clouds, rain, fog, etc., all of which restrict visibility. This skill is particularly useful when you fly long distances, e.g., over 300-500 NM. It is frequently difficult to travel such distances without encountering weather systems requiring instrument pilot skills. Similarly, if you must make a flight at a specific time, it may be possible only under instrument flight rules (IFR) due to adverse weather conditions.

Requirements to Obtain an Instrument Rating (Part 61)

1. Hold at least a private pilot certificate.
2. Be able to read, speak, write, and understand English.
3. Hold at least a current third-class FAA medical certificate.
4. Flight experience
   a. 50 hr. as pilot in command on cross-country flight (of which 10 hr. must be in airplanes) to airports more than 50 NM from the original departure point.
   b. 40 hr. of simulated or actual instrument time (of which up to 20 hr. can be in a flight simulator or flight training device; up to 10 hr. can be in an aviation training device).
   c. 15 hr. of instrument flight instruction in an airplane. This must be with a CFII (a CFI who has been certificated to instruct instrument flight).
5. Appropriate ground instruction (such as studying the Gleim *Instrument Pilot FAA Knowledge Test Prep* book, **FAA Test Prep Online**, and **Online Ground School**) to learn
   a. Federal regulations applicable to instrument pilots
   b. IFR navigation
   c. Aviation weather
   d. Safe and efficient flying skills applicable to IFR
   e. Aeronautical decision making and judgment
6. A score of 70% or better on the pilot knowledge test. The test consists of 60 multiple-choice questions. Sample FAA airplane questions are reproduced (with complete explanations to the right of each question) in the *Instrument Pilot FAA Knowledge Test Prep* book. The questions test the following 11 topics:
   a. Airplane Instruments
   b. Attitude Instrument Flying and Aerodynamics
   c. Navigation Systems
   d. Federal Aviation Regulations
   e. Airports, Air Traffic Control, and Airspace
   f. Holding and Instrument Approaches
   g. Aeromedical Factors
   h. Aviation Weather
   i. Aviation Weather Services
   j. IFR En Route
   k. IFR Flights

7. Flight instruction and development of the necessary skills to pass the instrument rating practical test. Your instrument instructor must provide a signed recommendation that you are competent as an instrument pilot.

8. Successful completion of the FAA Instrument Rating Practical Test. The FAA requires the following 20 tasks to be tested.

    a. Preflight Preparation

        1) Pilot Qualifications
        2) Weather Information
        3) Cross-Country Flight Planning

    b. Preflight Procedures

        1) Aircraft Systems Related to IFR Operations
        2) Aircraft Flight Instruments and Navigation Equipment
        3) Instrument and Equipment Cockpit Check

    c. Air Traffic Control Clearances and Procedures

        1) Compliance with Air Traffic Control Clearances
        2) Holding Procedures

    d. Flight by Reference to Instruments

        1) Instrument Flight
        2) Recovery from Unusual Flight Attitudes

    e. Navigation Systems

        1) Intercepting and Tracking Navigational Systems and DME Arcs
        2) Departure, En Route, and Arrival Operations

    f. Instrument Approach Procedures

        1) Nonprecision Approach (NPA)
        2) Precision Approach (PA)
        3) Missed Approach
        4) Circling Approach
        5) Landing from an Instrument Approach

    g. Emergency Operations

        1) Loss of Communications
        2) Approach with Loss of Primary Flight Instrument Indicators

    h. Postflight Procedures

        1) Checking Instruments and Equipment

Cost of Your Instrument Rating

Remember that you must have 50 hr. of cross-country time as pilot in command flying to airports more than 50 NM from the departure point. Rental rates for IFR-certified airplanes range from $50 to $180 per hour or more. Instrument instruction will cost about $40 to $60 per hour for your instructor (you are required to have 40 hr., but plan on at least 50 hr.). If you go to a typical FBO, you will probably spend $7,000 to $10,000 (not including your time building). As we recommend to prospective private pilots, you should discuss the cost with potential CFIIs. After you select a specific program, develop a budget with your CFII and review your progress periodically.

Once you have your private pilot certificate, it may be in your interest to purchase an IFR-equipped airplane or gain use of one through a flying club. For IFR certification, you need a full panel, which includes an attitude indicator, a heading indicator, a turn coordinator, and IFR-certified navigation equipment. As you are building cross-country hours toward your instrument rating, you should work on your instrument skills. It is more effective to proceed under the supervision of a CFII (flight instructor-instrument) than to try to do it entirely on your own.

1. **Ground trainers and Aviation Training Devices (ATDs)**. Several IFR flight simulators and Flight Training Devices have been marketed widely to colleges, FBOs, etc., as well as more-affordable ATDs. If you can gain access to one, use it under the supervision of a CFII who will sign off these hours in your logbook. Remember, up to 20 of the 40 hr. of required IFR experience and 10 of the 15 hr. of required instrument instruction may be in a flight simulator or a flight training device (only 10 of the required 40 hr. of instrument time may be obtained in an ATD).

2. **Safety pilots**. Once you have your private pilot certificate you can practice your instrument skills by using a "hood" (a view-limiting device so you can see your instruments but not outside of the airplane). **At all times** when you fly under the hood, you **must** have a safety pilot next to you watching for traffic. A safety pilot is appropriately rated to fly your airplane and is required by the Federal Aviation Regulations to look primarily for other air traffic (a midair collision would ruin your day). A safety pilot also can take over the controls if you get the airplane into an unusual attitude, i.e., if it begins to get out of control.

Steps to Take

1. Order the Gleim **Deluxe Instrument Pilot Kit with Online Ground School** from www.GleimAviation.com.

2. Take and pass the FAA pilot knowledge test (you need to answer 42 of the 60 FAA test questions correctly in order to pass). Use the ***Instrument Pilot FAA Knowledge Test Prep*** book, **FAA Test Prep Online**, and **Online Ground School**.

   a. Read the Introduction carefully.
   b. For each of the 12 study units,

      1) Study the outline at the beginning of the study unit.
      2) Read each FAA sample test question carefully and select the best answer.
      3) Check your answer with the correct answer next to each question.
      4) Read and understand our explanation of the question.

3. Study the Gleim ***Instrument Pilot Flight Maneuvers and Practical Test Prep*** book. Understand each aspect of IFR flight before you practice it in an airplane.

4. Pursue a flight instruction program with a CFII. When selecting a CFII, consider the suggestions on how to select a CFI (presented on page 7 of this booklet). One additional question to ask is how much actual IFR experience the CFII has. Another question is whether (s)he uses a simulator as a regular training tool.

5. Take and pass your practical test!

5.2 THE COMMERCIAL PILOT CERTIFICATE

A commercial pilot certificate is identical to your private pilot certificate except that it allows you to fly an airplane and carry passengers and/or cargo for compensation or hire. The certificate will be sent to you by the FAA upon satisfactory completion of your training program, a pilot knowledge test, and a practical test. Your commercial pilot certificate will be identical to your private pilot certificate, except it will indicate "commercial pilot" rather than "private pilot."

If you obtain your commercial pilot certificate before you obtain your multi-engine rating, your multi-engine rating practical test will be based on the commercial practical test standards, giving you a commercial pilot multi-engine rating rather than a private pilot multi-engine rating.

Requirements to Obtain a Commercial Pilot Certificate

1. Be at least 18 years of age.

2. Be able to read, speak, write, and understand English.

3. Hold at least a current third-class FAA medical certificate.

4. Hold an instrument rating. A commercial pilot is presumed to have an instrument rating. If not, his or her commercial pilot certificate will be endorsed with a prohibition against carrying passengers for hire on day VFR flights beyond 50 NM **or** at night.

5. Receive and log ground and flight training from an authorized instructor in the following areas of operations for an airplane.

    a. Preflight preparation
    b. Preflight procedures
    c. Airport operations
    d. Takeoffs, landings, and go-arounds
    e. Performance maneuvers
    f. Ground reference maneuver
    g. Navigation
    h. Slow flight and stalls
    i. Emergency operations
    j. High-altitude operations
    k. Postflight procedures

6. A score of 70% or better on the pilot knowledge test. The test consists of 100 multiple-choice questions. Sample FAA airplane questions are reproduced with complete explanations of each question in the Gleim *Commercial Pilot FAA Knowledge Test Prep* book, **FAA Test Prep Online**, and **Online Ground School**. The questions test the following 11 topics:

    a. Airplanes and Aerodynamics
    b. Airplane Instruments, Engines, and Systems
    c. Airports, Air Traffic Control, and Airspace
    d. Federal Aviation Regulations
    e. Airplane Performance and Weight and Balance
    f. Aeromedical Factors and Aeronautical Decision Making (ADM)
    g. Aviation Weather
    h. Aviation Weather Services
    i. Navigation: Charts, Publications, Flight Computers
    j. Navigation Systems
    k. Flight Operations

7. Flight experience. A total of 250 hr. of pilot flight time is required (with no more than 50 hr. in a flight simulator or flight training device). This must include the following:

    a. 100 hr. in powered aircraft, of which 50 hr. must be in airplanes

    b. 100 hr. as pilot in command flight time, which includes at least

        1) 50 hr. in airplanes
        2) 50 hr. in cross-country flight, of which 10 hr. must be in airplanes

    c. 20 hr. of flight training that includes at least

        1) 10 hr. of instrument training, of which at least 5 hr. must be in an airplane (not needed if you already hold an instrument rating)
        2) 10 hr. of training in an airplane that has a retractable landing gear, flaps, and controllable-pitch propeller, or is turbine-powered
        3) One cross-country flight of at least 2 hr. in an airplane in daytime conditions, consisting of a total straight-line distance of more than 100 NM from the original point of departure
        4) One cross-country flight of at least 2 hr. in an airplane in nighttime conditions, consisting of a straight-line distance of more than 100 NM from the original point of departure
        5) 3 hr. in an airplane in preparation for the practical test within the 2 calendar months preceding the test

    d. 10 hr. of solo flight in an airplane, which includes at least

        1) One cross-country flight of not less than 300 NM total distance, with landings at a minimum of three points, one of which is a straight-line distance of at least 250 NM from the original departure point

            a) In Hawaii, the longest segment need have only a straight-line distance of at least 150 NM.

        2) 5 hr. in night-VFR conditions with 10 takeoffs and 10 landings (with each landing involving a flight in the traffic pattern) at an airport with an operating control tower

8. Successful completion of an FAA practical test that will be given as a final exam. The practical test will be conducted as specified in the FAA's Airman Certification Standards. The maneuvers tested are the same as the maneuvers tested on the private practical test except five additional proficiency flight maneuvers are required: chandelles, eights on pylons, lazy eights, steep spirals, and a power-off precision landing. Two additional knowledge tasks are required: supplemental oxygen and pressurization. Obtain and study the Gleim *Commercial Pilot Flight Maneuvers and Practical Test Prep* book. It contains a reprint of tasks required on the commercial pilot practical test with a complete discussion and illustrations.

5.3 THE FLIGHT INSTRUCTOR CERTIFICATE

A flight instructor certificate allows you to give flight and ground training, i.e., to teach others to fly. An individual who wishes to have a career as a pilot typically earns the private, commercial, and flight instructor certificates (and an instrument rating). As a Certificated Flight Instructor (CFI), you can work as a flight instructor and get paid to teach aviation.

Requirements to Become a Certificated Flight Instructor (CFI)

1. Be at least 18 years of age.

2. Be able to read, write, and understand English.

3. Hold a commercial or ATP certificate.

    a. Hold an instrument rating if applying to be a flight instructor in an airplane.

4. Hold at least a current third-class FAA medical certificate.

5. A score of 70% or better on the FAA flight instructor knowledge test. The flight instructor test consists of 100 multiple-choice questions selected from the airplane-related questions in the FAA flight and ground instructor test bank. Sample FAA airplane questions are reproduced with complete explanations of each question in the Gleim *Flight/Ground Instructor FAA Knowledge Test Prep* book, **FAA Test Prep Online**, and **Online Ground School**. The questions test the following topics:

    a. Airplanes and Aerodynamics
    b. Airplane Performance
    c. Airplane Instruments, Engines, and Systems
    d. Airports, Airspace, and ATC
    e. Weight and Balance
    f. Aviation Weather
    g. Federal Aviation Regulations
    h. Navigation
    i. Flight Maneuvers
    j. Aeromedical Factors

6. A passing score on the FAA fundamentals of instructing knowledge test. It consists of 50 multiple-choice questions. The Gleim *Fundamentals of Instructing FAA Knowledge Test Prep* book, **FAA Test Prep Online**, and **Online Ground School** consist of a complete study program including questions similar to those that appear on the FAA knowledge test. The questions test the following topics:

    a. The Learning Process
    b. Barriers to Learning
    c. Factors Affecting Learning
    d. Teaching Methods
    e. Planning Instructional Activity
    f. Critique and Evaluation

NAFI (National Association of Flight Instructors)

Founded in 1967, NAFI is dedicated exclusively to raising and maintaining the professional standing of the flight instructor in the aviation community.

www.nafinet.org

SAFE (Society of Aviation and Flight Educators)

SAFE is a member-driven professional organization open to all aviation educators and provides members with mentoring, support, and professional accreditation.

www.SafePilots.org

7. Required Flight Instruction

   a. You must receive and log flight and ground training and obtain a logbook endorsement from an authorized instructor on the following areas of operations for an airplane category rating with a single-engine or multi-engine class rating.

      1) Fundamentals of instructing
      2) Technical support areas
      3) Preflight preparation
      4) Preflight lesson on a maneuver to be performed in flight
      5) Preflight procedures
      6) Airport operations
      7) Takeoffs, landings, and go-arounds
      8) Fundamentals of flight
      9) Performance maneuvers
      10) Ground reference maneuvers
      11) Slow flight, stalls, and spins
      12) Basic instrument maneuvers
      13) Emergency operations
      14) Postflight procedures

   b. The flight instruction must be given by a person who has held a flight instructor certificate during the 24 months immediately preceding the date the instruction is given and who has given at least 200 hr. of flight instruction as a CFI.

   c. You must also obtain a logbook endorsement by an appropriately certificated and rated flight instructor who has provided you with spin entry, spin, and spin recovery training in an airplane that is certificated for spins and has found you instructionally competent and proficient in those training areas, i.e., so you can teach spins.

8. Successful completion of a practical test that will be given as a final exam by an FAA inspector on the topics listed above. All of the tasks for the CFI are thoroughly explained as well as reprinted in the Gleim *Flight Instructor Flight Maneuvers and Practical Test Prep* book, which will provide you with step-by-step instructions for each flight maneuver. The flight portion of the practical test consists largely of those maneuvers tested on the commercial practical test except you must explain each maneuver to the examiner as you are flying the airplane. During the practical test, you will fly the airplane from the right seat because this is where CFIs instruct (with the student in the left seat).

Certificated Flight Instructor – Instrument (CFII)

In order to instruct pilots working toward their instrument rating, you must be an instrument instructor, which requires more training, another pilot knowledge test, and a practical test.

The FAA pilot knowledge test consists of 50 questions from the same questions used on the FAA pilot knowledge test for the instrument rating; i.e., you (in effect) retake your instrument rating knowledge test. Thus, you need to study and use the Gleim *Instrument Pilot FAA Knowledge Test Prep* book, **FAA Test Prep Online**, and **Online Ground School**.

The practical test consists of the instrument rating practical test maneuvers except you must explain the maneuvers as you perform them and you sit in the right seat. The Gleim *Instrument Pilot Flight Maneuvers and Practical Test Prep* book is an essential text to help you prepare for your CFII practical test.

CFIs NOTE: This is an excellent IFR refresher and update. Another major advantage is that passage of the flight test extends your CFI privileges for another 24 months; i.e., the additional rating both renews your CFI certificate and satisfies the flight review requirement.

5.4 THE AIRLINE TRANSPORT PILOT (ATP) CERTIFICATE

Airline transport pilots are responsible for operating large transport aircraft with advanced systems. To further your aviation career, or enter the airlines, achieving an ATP certificate is a must. ATP training will prepare you to fly according to the most demanding standards. The requirements vary depending on whether you will be flying single- or multi-engine airplanes. Airline pilots can enjoy many opportunities for a very rewarding career in aviation.

Requirements to Obtain an Airplane Transport Pilot Certificate

1. Be at least 23 years of age (at the time of the ATP practical test).

2. Be able to read, write, and converse in the English language.

3. Be of good moral character.

4. Hold at least a commercial pilot certificate and an instrument rating, a restricted ATP certificate, or a foreign ATP or commercial pilot certificate.

5. Hold at least a current FAA third-class medical certificate. Later, if your flying requires an ATP certificate, you must hold a first-class medical certificate.

6. Pass a pilot knowledge test with a score of 70% or better. The ATP multi-engine airplane test (ATM) consists of 125 multiple-choice questions selected from the airplane-related questions in the FAA's ATP, aircraft dispatcher, and flight navigator knowledge test bank.

    a. If you are seeking the ATP certificate with a multi-engine rating, you must complete an approved ATP Certification Training Program (CTP) in order to take the FAA knowledge test. A list of Gleim partnered ATP-CTP providers can be found at www.GleimAviation.com/atpctp.

    b. The ATP single-engine rating does not require completion of an ATP CTP.

    c. If you complete the ATP single-engine knowledge test (ATS) and then seek to add the multi-engine rating, you will be required to complete an ATP CTP program prior to taking the ATM knowledge test.

7. Accumulate flight experience consisting of at least 1,500 hours of total time as a pilot that includes at least

    a. 500 hours of cross-country flight time

    b. 100 hours of night flight time

    c. 50 hours of flight time in the class of airplane for the rating sought

    d. 75 hours of instrument flight time

    e. 250 hours of flight time in an airplane as a pilot in command, or as second in command performing the duties of pilot in command while under the supervision of a pilot in command, or any combination thereof, which includes at least

        1) 100 hours of cross-country flight time and
        2) 25 hours of night flight time.

    f. Additional requirements and allowances for simulator time are detailed in 14 CFR 61.159.

8. Successfully complete a practical flight test given as a final exam by an FAA inspector or designated pilot examiner and conducted as specified in the FAA's Airline Transport Pilot and Aircraft Type Rating Practical Test Standards.

REMOTE PILOT TRAINING

6.1 WHAT IS THE PART 107, SMALL UNMANNED AIRCRAFT RULE?

The Federal Aviation Administration (FAA) is part of the U.S. Department of Transportation. The FAA is responsible for the safety of civil aviation. This primarily includes airman certification, safety regulation, airspace and air traffic management, and aeronautical navigation.

Title 14 of the Code of Federal Regulations, Part 107, is the Small Unmanned Aircraft Rule. Part 107 contains the operational rules for routine commercial use of small unmanned aircraft systems (UAS, UAV, or "drones"). This rule includes operational limitations, requirements for certifications, responsibilities of the remote pilot in command, and aircraft requirements.

6.2 SUMMARY OF THE PART 107 REQUIREMENTS

1. **Operational Limitations**

    a. Unmanned aircraft must weigh less than 55 lb. (25 kg).

    b. Maximum groundspeed of 100 mph (87 knots).

    c. Maximum altitude of 400 feet above ground level (AGL) or, if higher than 400 feet AGL, remain within 400 feet of a structure.

    d. Visual line-of-sight (VLOS) only; the unmanned aircraft must remain within VLOS of the remote pilot in command and the person manipulating the flight controls of the small UAS.

    e. May use visual observer (VO) but not required. At all times, the small unmanned aircraft must remain close enough to the remote pilot in command and the person manipulating the flight controls of the small UAS for those people to be capable of seeing the aircraft with vision unaided by any device other than corrective lenses.

    f. First-person view camera cannot satisfy "see-and-avoid" requirement but can be used as long as requirement is satisfied in other ways.

    g. Small unmanned aircraft may not operate over any persons not directly participating in the operation, under a covered structure, or inside a covered stationary vehicle.

    h. Daylight-only operations or civil twilight (30 minutes before official sunrise to 30 minutes after official sunset, local time) with appropriate anti-collision lighting.

    i. Minimum weather visibility of 3 miles from control station.

    j. Operations in Class B, C, D, and E airspace may be allowed with the required ATC permission, which is obtained by getting a waiver from the FAA.

        1) Operations in Class G airspace are allowed without ATC permission.

    k.   Must yield right of way to other aircraft.

    l.   No person may act as a remote pilot in command or VO for more than one unmanned aircraft operation at one time.

    m.   No operations from a moving aircraft.

        1)   No operations from a moving vehicle unless the operation is over a sparsely populated area.

        2)   No careless or reckless operations.

    n.   A person may not operate a small unmanned aircraft if (s)he knows or has reason to know of any physical or mental condition that would interfere with the safe operation of a small UAS.

    o.   Foreign-registered small unmanned aircraft are allowed to operate under Part 107 if they satisfy the requirements of Part 375.

    p.   External load operations are allowed if the object being carried by the unmanned aircraft is securely attached and does not adversely affect the flight characteristics or controllability of the aircraft.

        1)   No carriage of hazardous materials.

    q.   Transportation of property for compensation or hire is allowed provided that

        1)   The aircraft, including its attached systems, payload, and cargo weigh less than 55 pounds total;

        2)   The flight is conducted within visual line of sight and not from a moving vehicle or aircraft; and

        3)   The flight occurs wholly within the bounds of a state and does not involve transport between

            a)   Hawaii and another place in Hawaii through airspace outside Hawaii;

            b)   The District of Columbia and another place in the District of Columbia;

            c)   A territory or possession of the United States and another place in the same territory or possession.

    r.   Most of the restrictions discussed above are waivable if the applicant demonstrates that his or her operation can safely be conducted under the terms of a certificate of waiver.

2.   **Remote Pilot in Command Certification and Responsibilities**

    a.   A person operating a small UAS must either hold a remote pilot airman certificate with a small UAS rating or be under the direct supervision of a person who does hold a remote pilot certificate (remote pilot in command).

    b.   To qualify for a remote pilot certificate, a person must

        1)   Demonstrate aeronautical knowledge by either

            a)   Passing an initial aeronautical knowledge test at an FAA-approved knowledge testing center or

            b)   Possessing a Part 61 pilot certificate other than student pilot, completing a flight review within the previous 24 months, and completing a small UAS online training course provided by the FAA.

        2)   Be vetted by the Transportation Security Administration.

        3)   Be at least 16 years old.

c.   Part 61 pilot certificate holders may obtain a temporary remote pilot certificate immediately upon submission of their application for a permanent certificate.

1)   Other applicants will obtain a temporary remote pilot certificate upon successful completion of TSA security vetting.

2)   The FAA anticipates that it will be able to issue a temporary remote pilot certificate within 10 business days after receiving a completed remote pilot certificate application.

d.   Until international standards are developed, foreign-certificated UAS pilots will be required to obtain an FAA issued remote pilot certificate with a small UAS rating.

e.   A remote pilot in command must

1)   Make available to the FAA, upon request, the small UAS for inspection or testing and any associated documents/records required to be kept under the rule.

2)   Report to the FAA within 10 days of any operation that results in at least serious injury, loss of consciousness, or property damage of at least $500.

3)   Conduct a preflight inspection, to include specific aircraft and control station systems checks, to ensure the small UAS is in a condition for safe operation.

4)   Ensure that the small unmanned aircraft complies with the existing registration requirements specified in 14 CFR 91.203(a)(2).

f.   A remote pilot in command may deviate from the requirements of this rule in response to an in-flight emergency.

3.   **Aircraft Requirements**

a.   FAA airworthiness certification is not required.

b.   The remote pilot in command must conduct a preflight check of the small UAS to ensure that it is in a condition for safe operation.

4.   **Model Aircraft**

a.   Part 107 does not apply to model aircraft that satisfy all of the criteria specified in section 336 of Public Law 112-95.

b.   The rule codifies the FAA's enforcement authority in Part 101 by prohibiting model aircraft operators from endangering the safety of the NAS.

6.3 TESTING REQUIREMENTS TO BECOME A REMOTE PILOT

1.   To become an FAA Certified Remote Pilot, you must pass a test.

   a.   If the applicant is not already a manned aircraft pilot certificated under 14 CFR Part 61, a knowledge test must be taken at an FAA-approved testing center.

   b.   If the applicant is already a pilot, an online test is required.

2.   The aeronautical knowledge subjects that will be tested for either testing method include

   a.   Regulations
   b.   Airspace classifications and requirements
   c.   Meteorology
   d.   Aircraft performance
   e.   Emergency operations
   f.   Crew resource management
   g.   Radio communication procedures
   h.   Human factors
   i.   Aeronautical decision making
   j.   Airport operations
   k.   Maintenance
   l.   Preflight inspections

3.   **First-time pilots**

   a.   If you are not already a pilot, you must first prepare for and pass the FAA Knowledge Test.

      1)   The test consists of 60 objective, multiple-choice questions.
      2)   There is a 2-hour time limit to complete the test.
      3)   There is a single correct response for each test question.
      4)   Each test question is independent of other questions.
      5)   A correct response to one question does not depend on, or influence, the correct response to another.

   b.   The test must be taken at an FAA-authorized testing center. These centers charge a fee to take the test.

4.   **Existing pilots** (Sport, Recreational, Private, Commercial, ATP)

   a.   If you are already a pilot, certificated under Part 61, and have a current flight review in accordance with 14 CFR 61.56, you must pass a FAASTeam online exam.

      1)   There is no fee to take the examination online.
      2)   If you do not have a current flight review, you must take the knowledge test at an authorized test center, using the same process as someone who is not a pilot.

5.   The complete steps to apply for the remote pilot certificate for both new and existing pilots are detailed at www.GleimAviation.com/drones.

6.4 COMMERCIAL sUAS APPLICATIONS

1. What can I do with a remote pilot certificate?

   a. The remote pilot certificate is your license to fly drones for hire.
   b. There are countless opportunities for sUAS, UAV, or drone operators.

      1) Photography and videography
      2) Real estate and construction
      3) Engineering
      4) Civil/government
      5) Aerial surveys
      6) Aerial inspections
      7) Agricultural
      8) Disaster relief
      9) Aviation training

MAINTENANCE OPERATIONS

7.1 PREVENTIVE MAINTENANCE AND INSPECTIONS

In aviation, flight is optional, but maintenance is mandatory. All U.S. certificated aircraft must undergo regular preventive maintenance and inspections. Most aircraft must undergo an annual inspection in addition to periodic inspections for certain installed equipment. As a general rule, the more complex the aircraft, the more maintenance is required. If an airplane is used for hire (flight instruction, cargo/personal charter, etc.), more frequent maintenance is necessary.

Like doctors, aviation mechanics tend to specialize in a particular area of aircraft maintenance. The table below identifies different specialties among aviation maintenance professionals. Most airports have some kind of maintenance operation on the field. The information in the table below shows you what to expect when you visit maintenance operations at your local airport.

Specialty	Description of Work	Experience/Certification Required
Fabric Covering	Repair structure as needed, apply fabric covering, and secure to the airframe. Shrink and treat fabric, apply color.	FAA Airframe Mechanic Certificate. Fabric work must be inspected before the airplane is flown.
Sheet Metal Repairs	Determine correct type of metal and fasteners required. Rivet, bolt, or screw into place as required by approved maintenance manuals.	Must hold an FAA issued Airframe Mechanic certificate. Major repairs must be inspected before flight.
Repairing Composite Structures	Remove damage, prepare area for repair, use correct materials and processes for repairs to cure properly.	Must hold an FAA issued Airframe Mechanic certificate. Major repairs must be inspected before flight.
Avionics Installation and Repair	Install units, connect electrical wiring, install antennas as required, amend airplane's weight and balance information to reflect the weight and location of new equipment	Technician must be trained by and work for a licensed repair facility or hold an FAA issued Airframe and Powerplant Mechanic certificate.
Turbine Engine Repair and Replacement	Repair and replace components or accessories based on approved practices published by the manufacturer. Formal classes and shop experience may be provided by the manufacturer to accomplish specific tasks.	Technician must be trained by and work for a licensed repair station or hold an FAA Powerplant Mechanic certificate.
Engine Overhaul	Remove and disassemble the unit. Inspect thoroughly. Repair or replace worn or damaged parts. Reassemble and reinstall in accordance with approved or accepted standards.	Technician must be trained by and work for a licensed repair station or hold an FAA issued Powerplant Mechanic certificate to overhaul an engine.
Propeller Overhaul	Inspect and repair or replace worn or damaged parts included in the propeller unit.	Technician must be trained by and work for a licensed repair station to make major repairs to propellers.
Paint and Interior Modifications	Prepare surfaces, tape patterns, apply paint and sealers. Interior work ranges from installing seats to plumbing lavatories and building galleys.	Technician must be trained by and work for a licensed repair station. Work will be inspected by certified mechanics before flight.
Maintenance on Homebuilt Experimental Aircraft	Inspect airframe and engine completely, including all cables, connectors, structures, skins, fasteners, engine compression, and propeller.	Must hold an FAA issued Airframe and Powerplant certificate or a Repairman Certificate for the specific aircraft.

7.2 HAZARDS

When visiting a maintenance facility, be careful to stand only where you are instructed. There can be a number of potentially unseen hazards in the workspace. Use caution and follow the instructions of the person escorting you. If you ever doubt that you are in a safe location, ALWAYS ask immediately.